Contents

Special Features

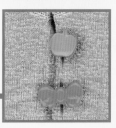
Features

Buttons

Written by Karen Anderson

A telephone has buttons.

Telephone buttons

A stereo has buttons.

Stereo
buttons

A remote control has buttons.

Remote-control buttons

A television has buttons.

Television
buttons

A microwave has buttons.

Microwave buttons

Safari
WORD POWER

 Aa
 Bb
 Cc
 Dd
 Ee
 Ff
 Gg
 Hh
 Ii

 Zz
 Yy
 Xx
 Ww
 Vv
 Uu
 Tt
 Ss
 Rr

my   A   has

My

I   a

the   am

Find –
A a am has
I My my the

 Jj   Kk   Ll    Mm   Nn   Oo    Pp   Qq

8

Jumping Buttons

Written by Simone Santo
Illustrated by Trevor Pye

Jump and land,
Jump and land,
Jump and land,
In the sand!

Jump and land,
Jump and land,
Jump and land,
In my hand!

band
grand
hand
land
sand
stand
band
grand
hand
land
sand
stand
band
grand
hand
land
sand
stand

band
grand
hand
land
sand
stand
band
grand
hand
land
sand
stand
band
grand
hand
land
sand
stand

9

Buttons, Buttons, Buttons

Written by Josephine Selwyn

My doll has buttons.

My bear has buttons.

My flute has buttons.

My drum has buttons.

My telephone has buttons.

My bowl
has buttons.

Buttons, buttons, buttons.

Where Are We?

Written by Cory Winesap

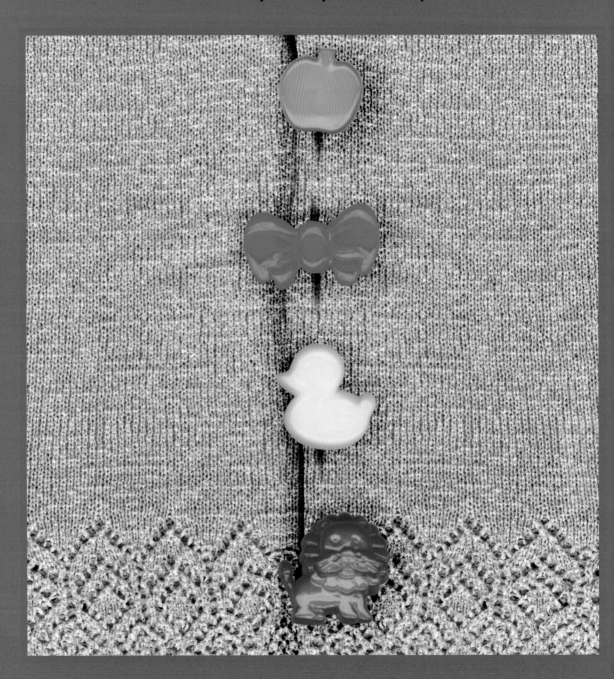

Button 1

I am a red button.

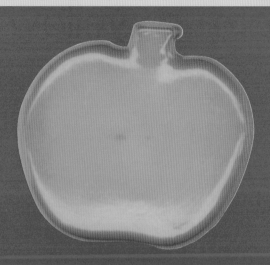

 ## Button 2

I am a blue button.

Button 3

I am a yellow button.

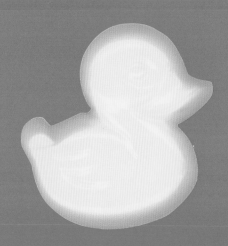

Button 4

I am a green button.

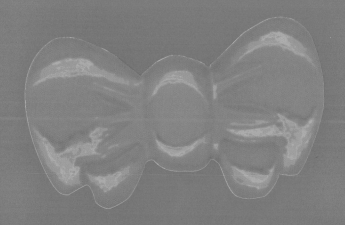

Button 1

I look like an apple.

Button 2

I look like a lion.

Button 3

I look like a duck.

Button 4
I look like a bow.

Buttons

 1

 2

 3

 4

Where are we?

The Button Band

Written by Michele Ashley
Illustrated by Helen Casey

Button Band,
Play on the sand.
Button Band,
Play on the land.

Play on the sand,
Play on the land.
The Button Band
Sounds really grand!

readingsafari.com

Check out these Safari magazines, too!

Have your say –

e-mail your Safari Tour Guide at
tourguide@readingsafari.com

Safari Tour Guide,

 40

I made a pattern with some buttons. Shall I draw it for you?

Jessie Smith (6)

Find some fun things to do!

Go to –
http://www.readingsafari.com

Safari Superstar

Name – Rockin' Bob Button

Birthday – January 7

Find out more about this Safari Superstar at
http://www.readingsafari.com

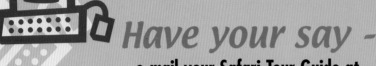

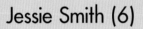

24